Instant Art for Bible Worksheets

Book 5

Compiled by Michael Forster
and
Illustrated by Arthur Baker

First published in 1995 in Great Britain by
KEVIN MAYHEW LTD
Rattlesden
Bury St Edmunds, Suffolk IP30 0SZ

Catalogue No 1396039
ISBN 0 86209 731 2

Cover by Sara Silcock
Typesetting and page creation by Louise Hill
Printed in Great Britain

Introduction

Following the success of Books 1, 2, 3 and 4 in the *Instant Art for Bible Worksheets* series, we are delighted to offer a fifth collection.

As before, these sheets are intended to be a resource for a variety of applications: family services, Sunday schools, mid-week clubs, holiday clubs and for use in day schools. They have been designed so that children of varying ages and abilities can use them at their own level, although in conjunction with, and not in place of, an accompanying talk.

• day school use

The worksheets lend themselves to follow-up work from a school or class assembly or a class lesson, for which they can be adapted, if necessary.

For the infant age group, the word search puzzles could either be deleted altogether or replaced by a simple word exercise. For the junior age group, the picture could be replaced by comprehension questions, multi-choice answer questions or similar exercises.

• photocopy/cut out

Unlike some of the titles in the 'Instant Art' series, this book has been compiled as a collection of single page worksheets, the assumption being that users will reproduce a particular page (as a unit) in the quantities they require. However, individual items could be combined with other material and used in whatever way is most helpful. Our aim continues to be to provide material that is versatile and flexible in use.

As before, the pages have been printed on one side only to give the best possible quality of reproduction from a photocopier. The book's format allows it to be placed flat on the photocopier.

• Bible editions

We have used the *New International Version* or the *Good News Bible*, the two editions which our research shows are the most commonly used by children.

• contents

A list of worksheets contained in this collection, together with scriptural references and page numbers, is given overleaf.

• copyright

Material in this book is copyright-free provided that it is used for the purpose for which the book is intended. The usual copyright restrictions apply to any use for *commercial* purposes.

Users' Responses

Sales of books in the 'Instant Art' series continue to prove that they are meeting a need. The series is now developing in response to, and with the help of, people who have found material in the existing books useful. Your ideas or suggestions for new titles would be warmly received and carefully considered!

Contents

Read this story in Genesis 13

Bring the Jordan Valley to life by colouring it.

Show Lot and his party the way to Sodom.

Spot six differences

Wordsearch

EGYPT
CANAAN
LOT
ABRAM
BETHEL
AI
CANAANITES
PERIZZITES
JORDAN
ZOAR

C	L	O	T	P	Z	M	A	R	B
X	A	D	R	O	J	L	G	A	B
A	M	N	A	D	R	O	J	Y	E
B	T	R	A	P	E	R	I	Z	T
R	P	X	C	A	N	A	A	N	H
A	Y	C	A	I	N	A	O	R	E
Y	G	J	O	R	D	I	X	B	L
P	E	R	I	Z	Z	I	T	E	S
C	A	N	A	M	L	D	Z	E	I
E	F	M	A	R	B	A	O	N	S

Read this story in Genesis 14:8-16

Lot is taken prisoner

Lot is pleased that Abram has rescued him. The Pictures may look the same, but can you find ten differences between them?

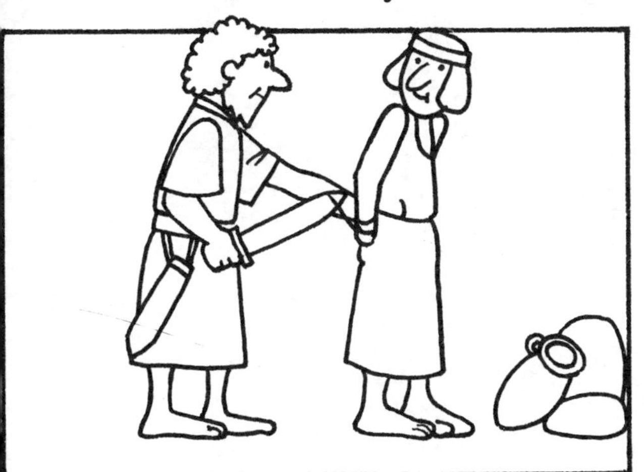

Help Abram rescue the prisoners.

Isaac is born

Palm Tree Worksheet 3

Read this story in Genesis 21

They're celebrating. Can you find six bottles of wine?

For God everything is possible

Mark 10:27

Crack the code

Join the dots to find the baby.

Help the baby find his balloon.

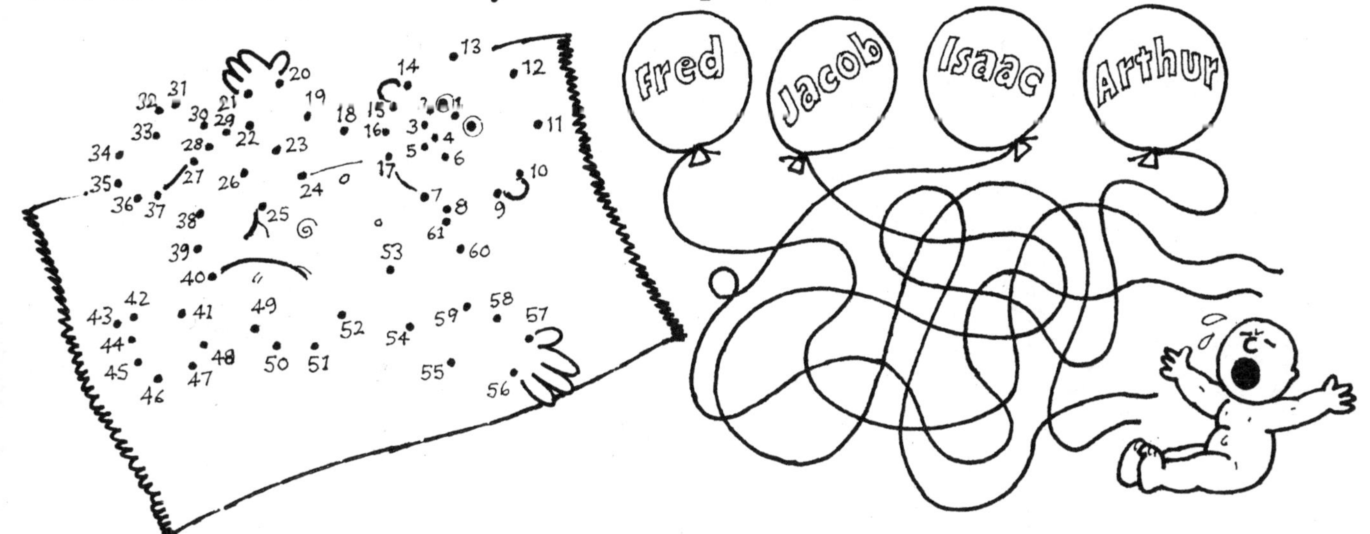

Read this story in Genesis 23

Abraham bargains with Ephron

Be good neighbours

Can you make the words fit?

MACHPELAH
ABRAHAM
SARAH
EPHRON
ZOHAR
HEBRON
CANAAN
CAVE
HITTITES

Join the dots to make the cave, and then lead Abraham to it.

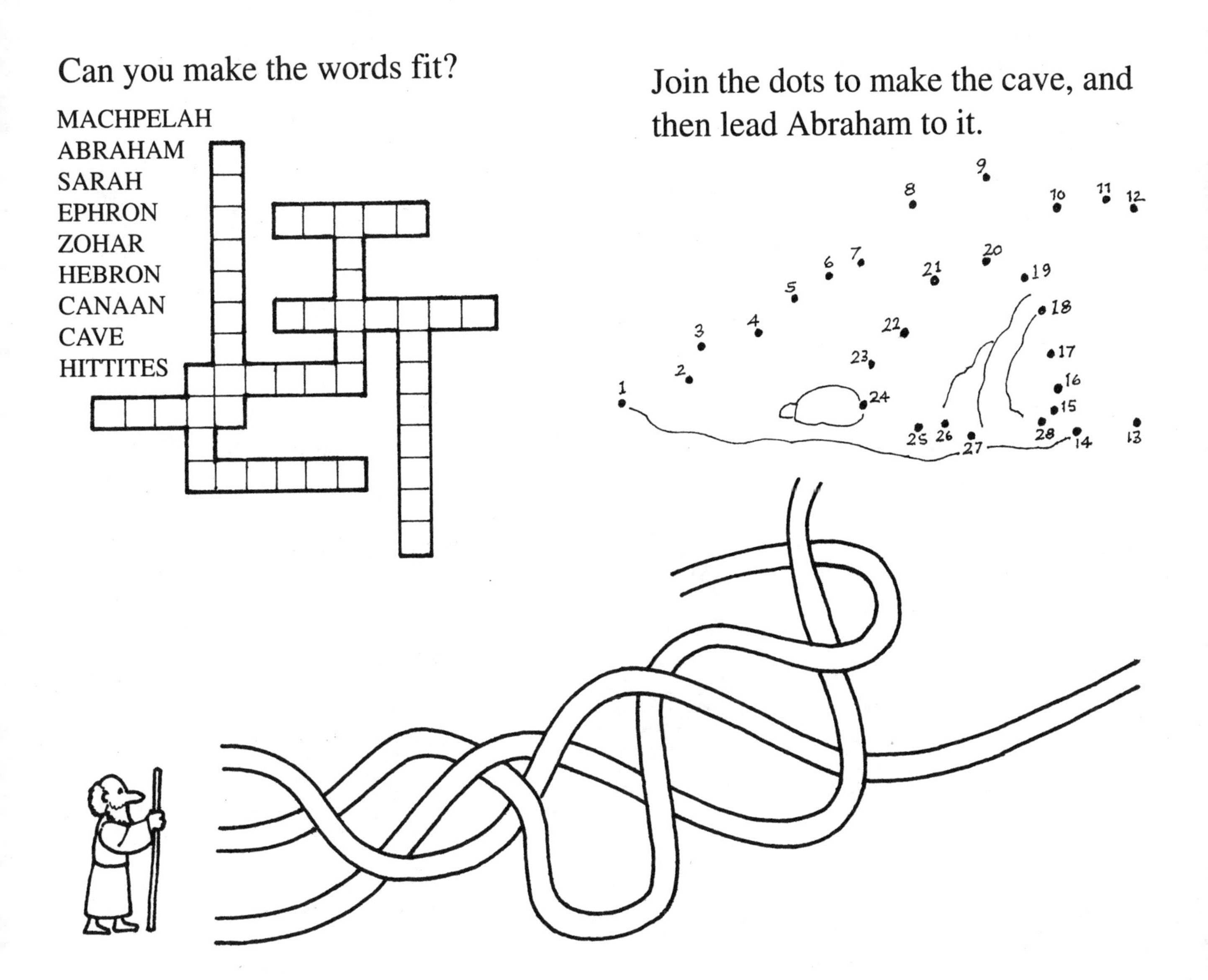

Read this story in Genesis 26:12-25

Isaac has lots of sheep. He is very rich, and the Philistines are jealous. Can you find their six spies in the picture?

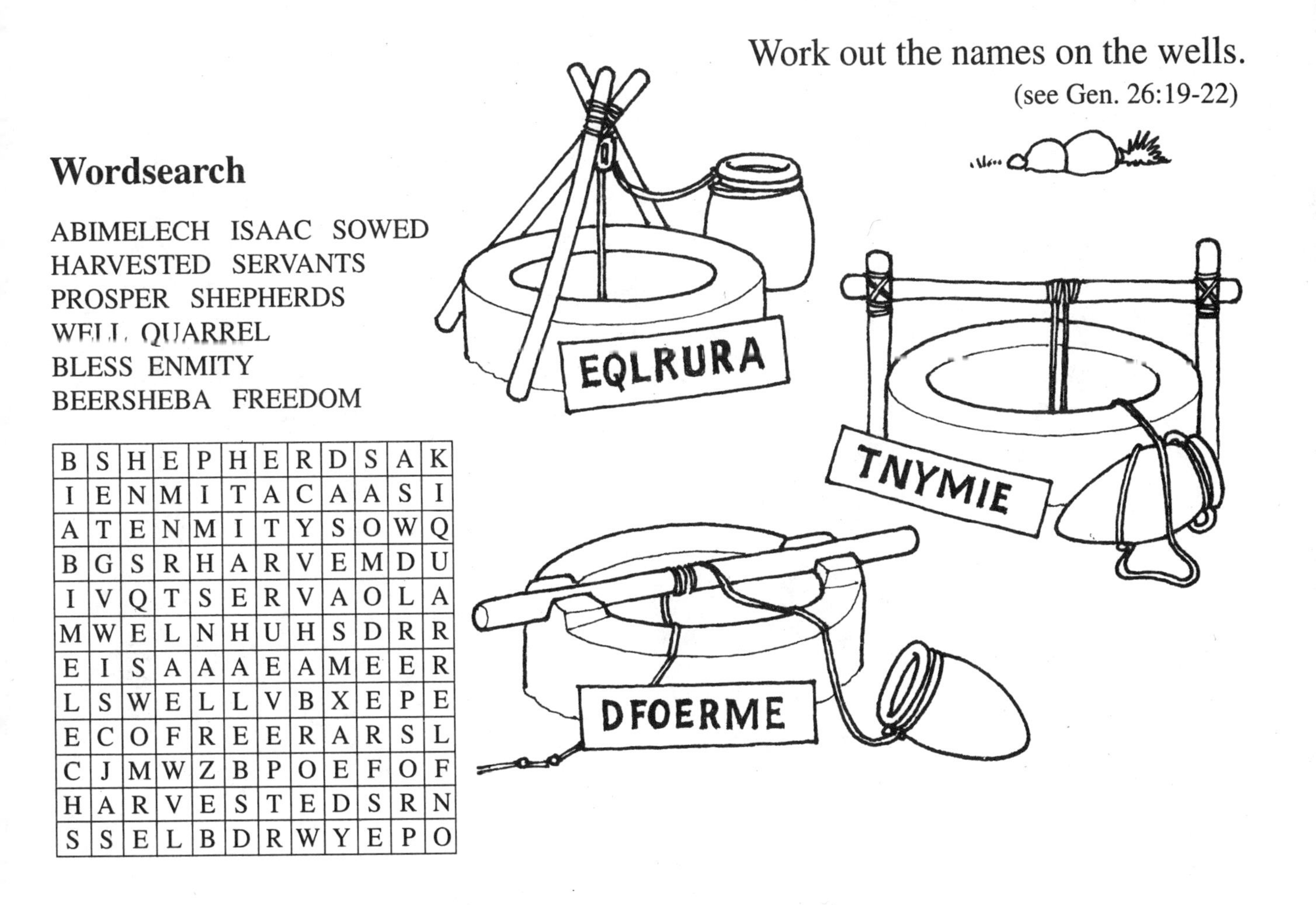

Work out the names on the wells.
(see Gen. 26:19-22)

Wordsearch

ABIMELECH ISAAC SOWED
HARVESTED SERVANTS
PROSPER SHEPHERDS
WELL QUARREL
BLESS ENMITY
BEERSHEBA FREEDOM

B	S	H	E	P	H	E	R	D	S	A	K
I	E	N	M	I	T	A	C	A	A	S	I
A	T	E	N	M	I	T	Y	S	O	W	Q
B	G	S	R	H	A	R	V	E	M	D	U
I	V	Q	T	S	E	R	V	A	O	L	A
M	W	E	L	N	H	U	H	S	D	R	R
E	I	S	A	A	A	E	A	M	E	E	R
L	S	W	E	L	L	V	B	X	E	P	E
E	C	O	F	R	E	E	R	A	R	S	L
C	J	M	W	Z	B	P	O	E	F	O	F
H	A	R	V	E	S	T	E	D	S	R	N
S	S	E	L	B	D	R	W	Y	E	P	O

Read this story in Genesis 47:1-12

Joseph introduces Jacob to the king

Unscramble the words, and then draw a line from each label to the right food.

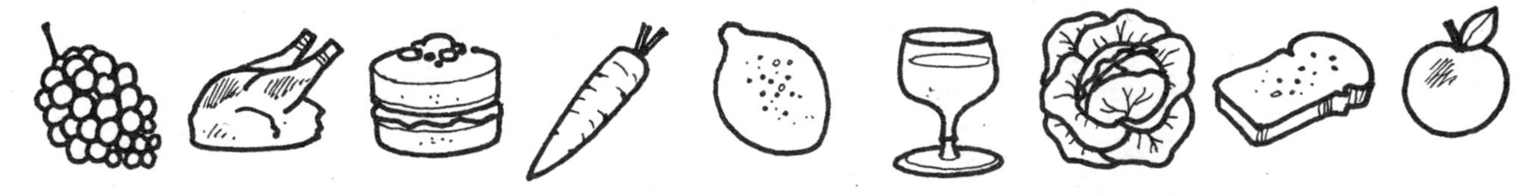

KCNICEH PEPLA ENMLO BCBEAGA KAEC RPGSAE DEBAR EINW ATROCR

What a relief! Jacob's wanderings are over.

These pictures may look the same, but can you spot ten differences?

Moses, Aaron and Pharaoh

Palm Tree Worksheet 7

Read this story in Exodus 5

Pharaoh's secret agents are watching Moses and Aaron. Can you see them?

Crack the code

1	2	3	4	5	6	7	8	9	0	*
A	D	E	G	L	N	O	P	S	T	Y

4	7	2		9	1	*	9

5	3	0		6	*		8	3	7	8	5	3		4	7

Lead the slaves to freedom.

Read this story in Exodus 13:17-22

The Lord is my light

Psalm 27:1

Some things the Bible says about light

God divided the light from the _ _ _ _ _ _ _ _. (Genesis 1:4)
You will see the _ _ _ _ _ _ _ _ light of the Lord's presence. (Exodus 16:7)
It is good to be able to _ _ _ _ _ the pleasant light of _ _ _. (Ecclesiastes 11:7)
Your _ _ _ _ are like a _ _ _ _ for the body. (Luke 11:34)
Whoever does what is _ _ _ _ comes to the _ _ _ _ _. (John 3:21)
I am the _ _ _ _ _ of the _ _ _ _ _. (John 9:5)

Using crayons, turn one of these pictures into night, and the other into day.

Water from the rock

Palm Tree Worksheet 9

Read this story in Exodus 17:1-7

Do not put the Lord to the test

Matthew 4:7

Where can we get water from?

What can we use water for?

Can you spot six differences in these pictures?

Read this story in Exodus 18:1-12

Praise the Lord who saves

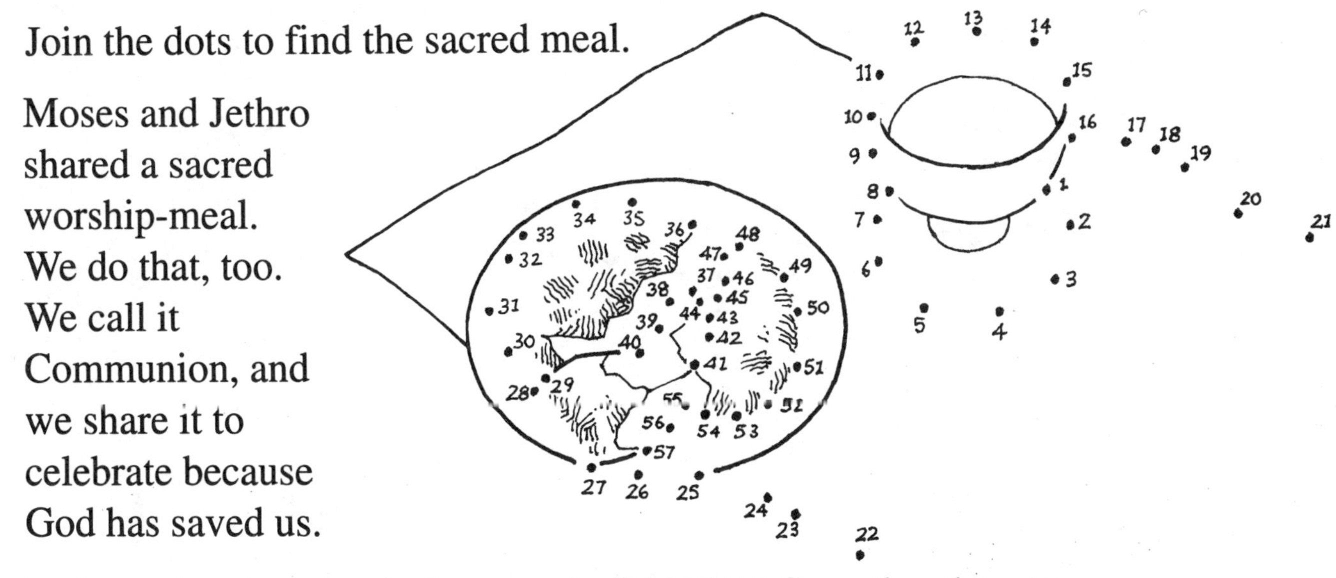

Join the dots to find the sacred meal.

Moses and Jethro shared a sacred worship-meal. We do that, too. We call it Communion, and we share it to celebrate because God has saved us.

Substitute rhyming words for ones in CAPITALS, so that the sentences make sense.

Christians share FED _ _ _ _ _ and LINE _ _ _ _ as a sign that God SHOVES _ _ _ _ _ us and that we SHOVE _ _ _ _ one another. We are all OTHERS _ _ _ _ _ _ _ _ and BLISTERS _ _ _ _ _ _ _ in God's family, and this is our HEEL _ _ _ _ . We eat and drink WEATHER _ _ _ _ _ _ _ _ at God's CABLE _ _ _ _ _ to remember Jesus, until he comes RAIN _ _ _ _ _ .

Read this story in Exodus 18:14-27

Replace the words in CAPITALS with other, rhyming words so that the passage makes sense!

ROSES _ _ _ _ _ was the FEEDER _ _ _ _ _ _ of the STEEPLE _ _ _ _ _ _ of Israel. Jethro was his LIFE'S _ _ _ _'_ RATHER _ _ _ _ _ _ _. Jethro told POSIES _ _ _ _ _ to appoint GRUDGES _ _ _ _ _ _ to help him COOL _ _ _ _ the STATION _ _ _ _ _ _ _. The FUDGES _ _ _ _ _ _ would DERIDE _ _ _ _ _ _ who was LIGHT _ _ _ _ _ and who was SONG _ _ _ _ _. This would save HOSES _ _ _ _ _ SHIRK _ _ _ _ so that he wouldn't get FIRED _ _ _ _ _.

Join the dots to find the judge.

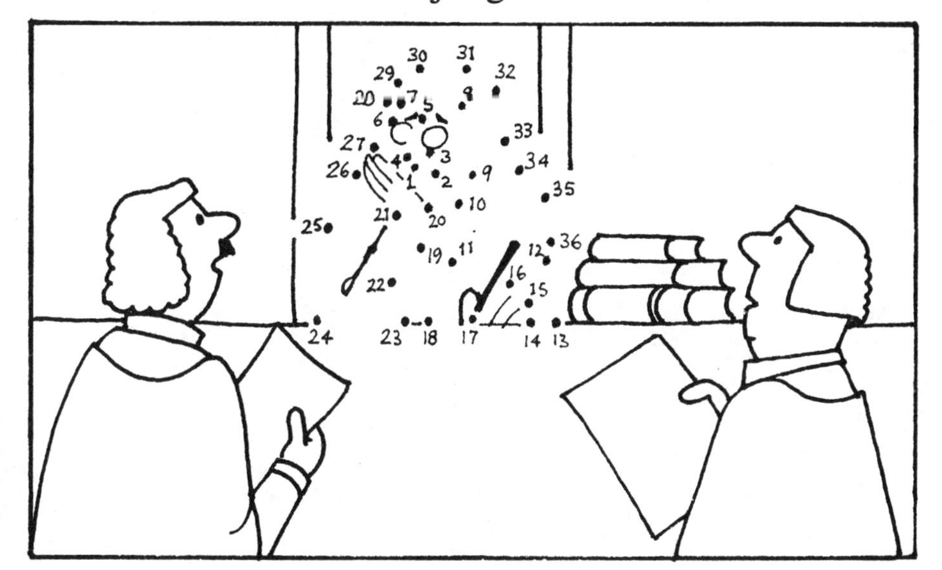

Wordsearch

HUNDREDS THOUSANDS FIFTIES TENS JETHRO MOSES JUDGES DISPUTES

D	F	F	I	F	T	I	E	S	B
Q	J	H	U	N	D	R	E	X	I
S	D	E	R	D	N	U	H	J	S
N	F	N	T	M	O	S	E	F	E
E	I	A	E	H	T	T	E	N	T
T	F	T	H	O	R	S	A	N	U
H	T	K	S	E	S	O	M	O	P
P	O	S	E	G	D	U	J	C	S
L	E	Q	S	M	U	I	R	G	I
T	H	O	U	S	A	N	D	S	D

Read this story in Exodus 19:1-13

Obey me and keep my covenant

Exodus 19:5

As we worship, so must we live. Should we: (✓ for yes, ✘ for no)

Read this story in Exodus 25:10-22

Help the craftsmen find their tools: a saw, a hammer a chisel and a paintbrush.

Join the dots to draw the Ark.

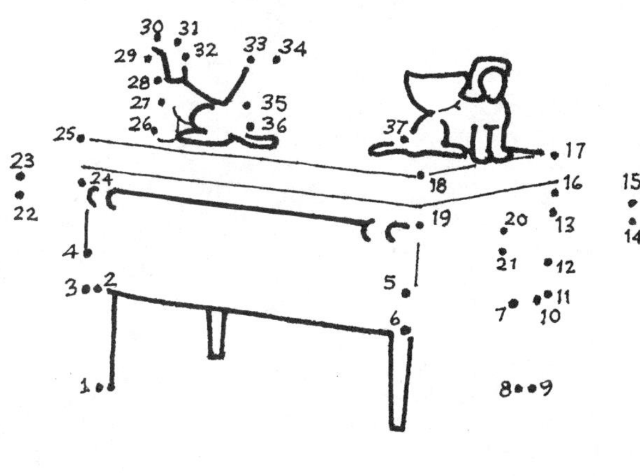

B	T	D	E	G	N	I	W	U	I	F	H
N	R	L	S	T	E	L	B	A	T	Q	A
C	O	M	M	E	N	D	M	E	X	O	M
T	K	E	Q	P	R	O	H	Y	A	N	M
N	T	A	B	L	E	U	X	D	E	A	E
A	M	G	O	L	T	X	T	B	L	W	R
N	J	C	O	V	E	N	A	A	X	F	E
E	V	K	C	L	P	C	O	M	E	I	D
V	H	A	M	M	D	D	G	S	H	R	Z
O	C	R	E	A	T	U	R	Y	L	C	O
C	O	M	M	A	N	D	M	E	N	T	S
W	I	N	G	A	C	A	C	I	A	G	J

Wordsearch

ACACIA
COMMANDMENTS
CREATURES
WINGED
HAMMERED
GOLD
COVENANT
TABLETS

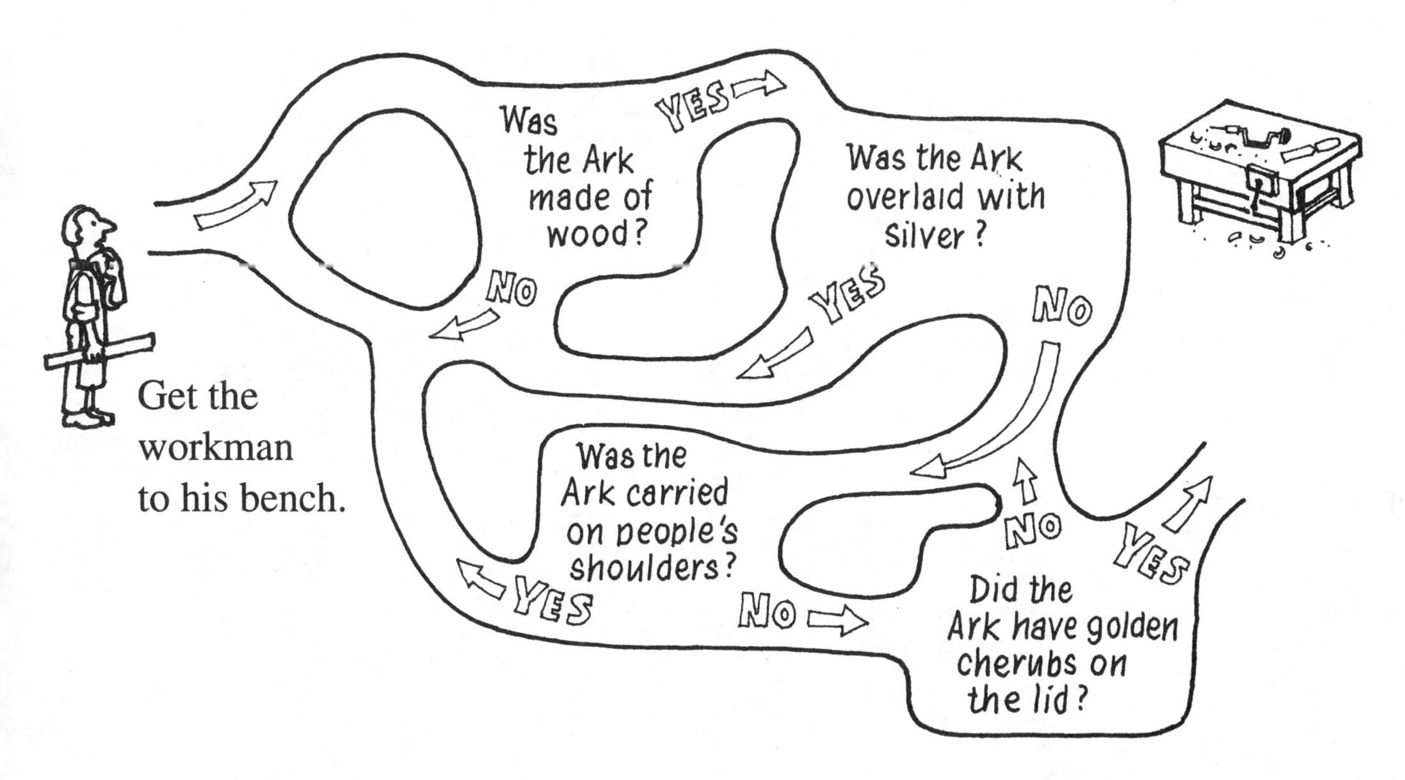

Get the workman to his bench.

Read about this in Leviticus 25:8-17

Help the trumpeter find his trumpet.

Crack the code

Y	U	T	R	O	N	L	I	F	E	D	A
A	D	E	F	I	L	N	O	R	T	U	Y

U	I		L	I	E		U	T	Y	N		D	L	R	Y	O	F	N	A

Wordsearch:
foods which grow wild

BLACKBERRIES STRAWBERRIES
CRABAPPLES BILBERRIES
MUSHROOMS CHESTNUTS
THYME HIPS
HAWS

B	L	A	C	K	B	E	R	R	I	E	S
L	S	E	L	P	P	A	B	A	R	C	E
A	S	E	N	C	T	H	Y	M	X	O	I
C	M	C	I	P	F	C	A	Q	T	V	R
K	O	H	S	R	U	L	N	W	J	H	R
B	O	E	X	I	R	Y	B	P	S	K	E
E	R	S	A	G	Q	E	J	T	D	F	B
R	H	T	H	Y	M	E	B	U	V	S	W
L	S	N	A	E	L	I	O	L	R	D	A
M	U	U	S	H	R	O	P	N	I	W	R
B	M	T	Z	E	M	R	M	Z	G	B	T
H	K	S	T	R	A	W	B	H	I	P	S

Help the slave find his way home.

Read about this in Leviticus 26:1-13

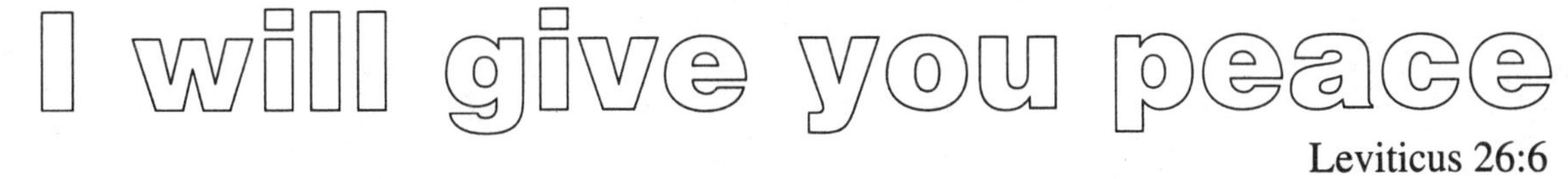

Leviticus 26:6

Crack the code. You have a problem: one letter is missing from the code. Can you work it out? (Do the ones you can, first)

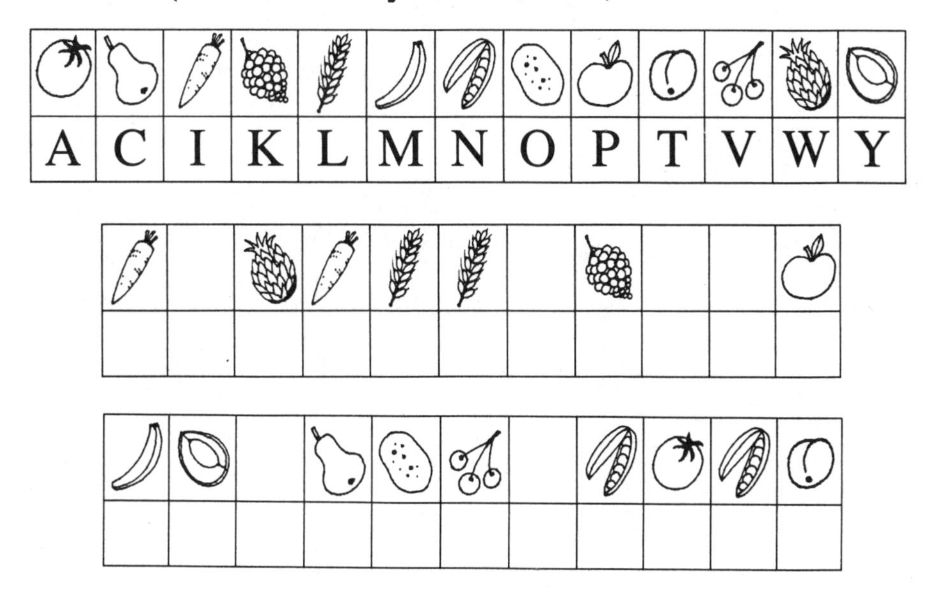

Find rhymes for the words in CAPITALS, to make the sentence make sense.

If you live according to my PAWS _ _ _ _ and obey my HANDS _ _ _ _ _ _ _ _ I will send you PAIN _ _ _ _ so that the BAND _ _ _ _ will produce BOPS _ _ _ _ _ which will be so plentiful that you will still be harvesting TORN _ _ _ _ when it is time to STICK _ _ _ _ NAPES _ _ _ _ _ _ _ _ .

Read this story in 1 Samuel 8

I am the one they have rejected

1 Samuel 8:7

God gave the people:	The king would give them:
ECAEP	RAW
MODEERF	YREVALS
YTIREPSORP	YTREVOP
EVOL	NOITAXAT

The poor man has lost his six best sheep. Can you find them in the palace garden?

Read this story in 1 Samuel 16:14-23

Crack the code to find a song David wrote.

♬	♯	𝅝	♭	𝄢	♩	♩♪	𝄼	𝄽	2/4	♮	*pp*
D	E	H	I	L	M	O	P	R	S	T	Y

♮	𝅝	♯		𝄢	♩♪	𝄽	♬		♭	2/4

♩	*pp*		2/4	𝅝	♯	𝄼	𝅝	♯	𝄽	♬

Colour the dotted shapes to find the goat.

Wordsearch

SAUL JESSE BETHLEHEM
MUSICIAN TORMENTED
DAVID

M	U	S	I	C	I	A	N	B	D
E	X	B	E	T	H	E	O	E	A
H	U	Q	C	S	X	L	W	T	V
E	D	A	V	I	S	S	I	H	I
L	T	U	R	M	E	E	X	L	D
H	Y	D	E	T	G	K	J	E	V
T	D	E	T	N	E	M	R	O	T
E	E	R	D	A	V	I	X	J	B
B	Z	A	S	A	U	L	Y	Q	L
M	U	S	I	C	I	A	F	F	H

Read this story in 1 Samuel 26

Happy are those who are merciful

Matthew 5:7

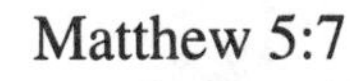

Can you find ten differences in these pictures?

Help David and Abishai to find Saul.

Read this story in 2 Samuel 5

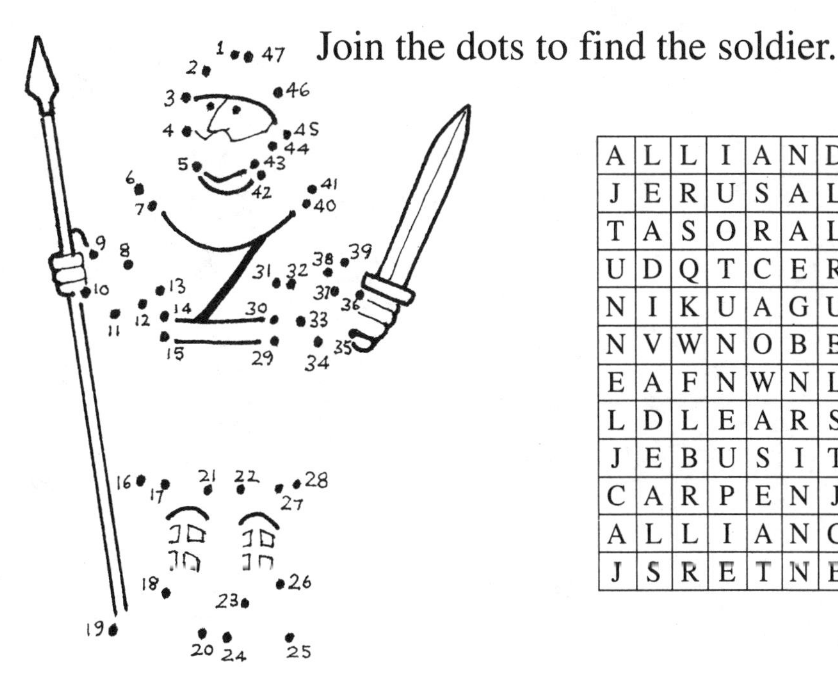

Join the dots to find the soldier.

Wordsearch

A	L	L	I	A	N	D	A	V	I	X	F
J	E	R	U	S	A	L	E	M	E	J	O
T	A	S	O	R	A	L	L	I	A	E	R
U	D	Q	T	C	E	R	D	P	H	B	T
N	I	K	U	A	G	U	L	Y	E	U	R
N	V	W	N	O	B	B	Q	H	B	S	E
E	A	F	N	W	N	L	U	N	R	I	S
L	D	L	E	A	R	S	I	M	O	T	S
J	E	B	U	S	I	T	E	S	N	C	X
C	A	R	P	E	N	J	E	B	H	X	P
A	L	L	I	A	N	C	E	I	T	E	S
J	S	R	E	T	N	E	P	R	A	C	D

JERUSALEM
HEBRON
DAVID
CONQUER
JEBUSITES
FORTRESS
ESTABLISHED
CARPENTERS
ALLIANCE
ISRAEL
TUNNEL

Which tunnel should David choose?

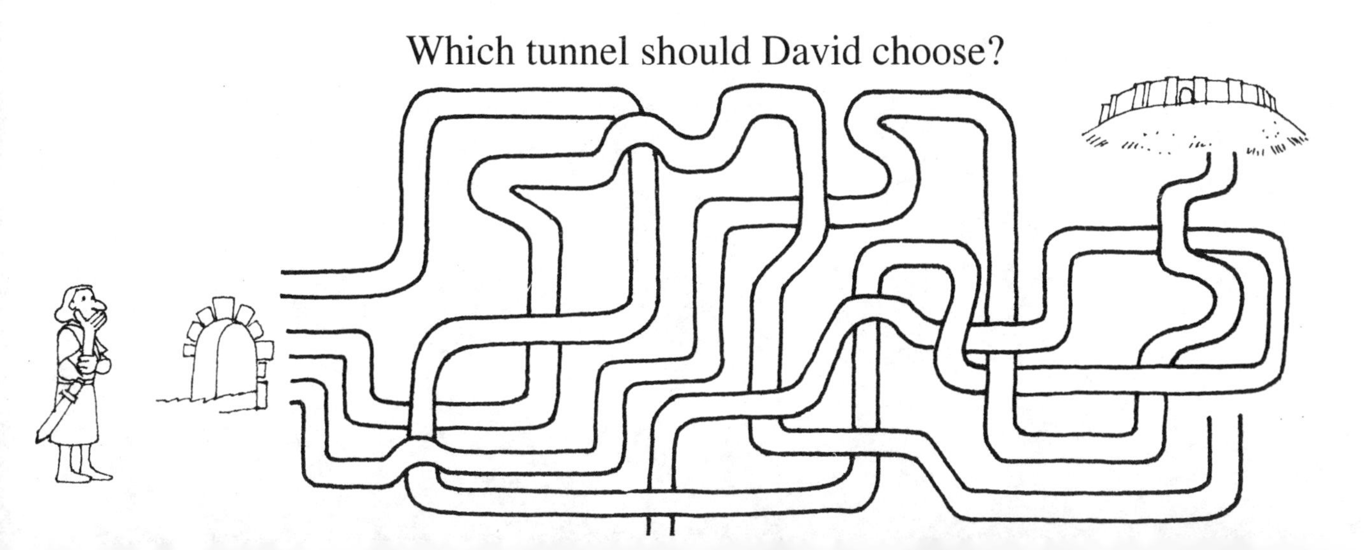

Read this story in 1 Kings 3:1-14

It is the Lord who gives wisdom

Proverbs 2:6

Why did Solomon want wisdom?

☐ To make him rich?
☐ To make him famous?
☐ To help him govern fairly?
☐ To save him working?
☐ To give him long life?

Solomon was a good ruler.

Would he be:

Greedy?

Kind?

Join the dots to find Solomon.

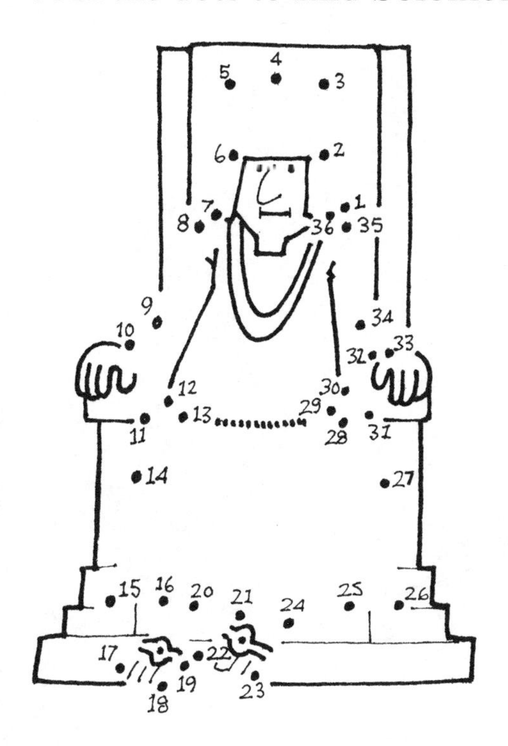

Cruel?

Generous?

Proud?

Humble?

Read this story in 1 Kings 8

The Lord has kept his promise

1 Kings 8:20

Use a rhyming word for each one in CAPITALS to make sense of the sentences.

Solomon brought God's SOCKS _ _ _ to the temple.
He sacrificed BLEEP _ _ _ _ _ and RATTLE _ _ _ _ _ _ _ .
The box was put in the most holy BRACE _ _ _ _ _ beneath the RINGED _ _ _ _ _ _ creatures.
Solomon said that God had placed the BUN _ _ _ in the PIE _ _ _ .
Solomon said that God had chosen to live in the CROWDS _ _ _ _ _ _ _ .

Get the box into the holy of holies.

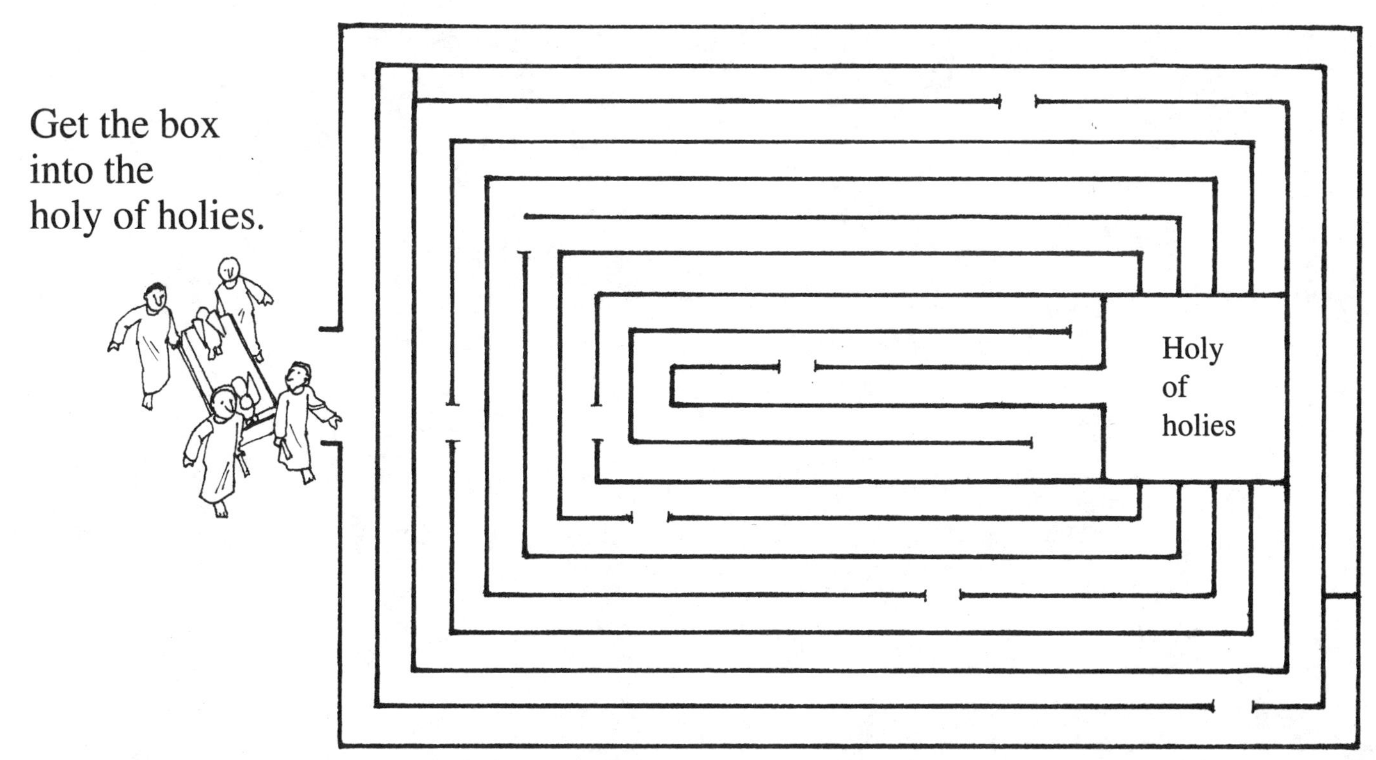

Read this story in 1 Kings 10:1-13

These two pictures may look the same, but can you find ten differences?

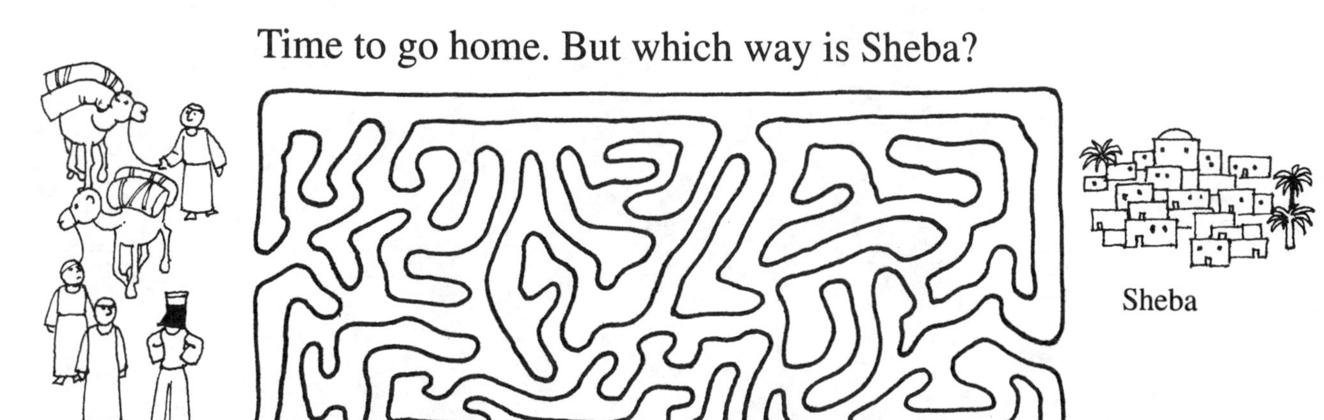

Read about this in 1 Kings 10:14-25

Look how the wild flowers grow

Luke 12:27

Crack the code to find a saying of Jesus.

D	E	G	K	N	O	R	S	U	W

These pictures may look the same, but can you find ten differences?

Micaiah tells the truth

Palm Tree Worksheet 24

Read this story in 1 Kings 22:1-28

Micaiah prophesies to the kings

Tell the truth!

see 1 Kings 22:16

Micaiah was the only truthful one. Find the odd one out in each picture.

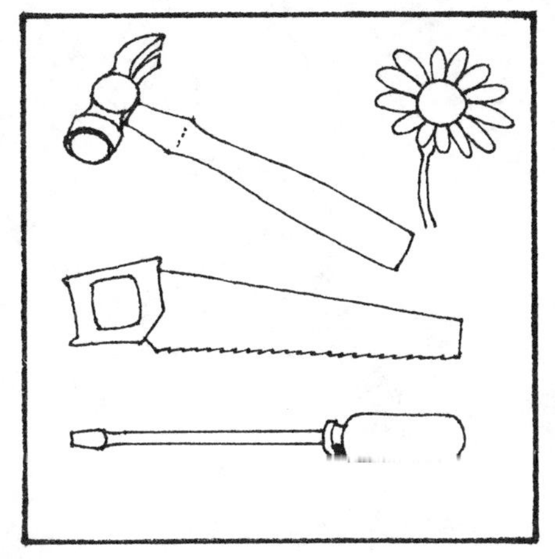

Place these words horizontally on the grid to find the motto running down the centre.
(The first one has been done for you)

MICAIAH
JEHOSHAPHAT
RETURN
PEACE
AHAB
PROPHETS
SYRIANS
CHENAANAH

Read this story in 2 Kings 2:1-14

I will not leave you

2 Kings 2:2

Wordsearch:

ELIJAH ELISHA HORSES
CHARIOTS FIRE
FIFTY ISRAEL
CLOAK PROPHETS
JERICHO DEFENDER
SHARE POWER
STRUCK WHIRLWIND
GILGAL LOYALTY

S	C	H	A	R	I	O	S	H	A	R	E
T	L	O	Y	A	L	T	Y	I	S	R	A
E	C	H	A	R	I	O	T	S	F	I	F
H	C	L	O	A	O	H	C	I	R	E	J
P	E	I	J	A	S	A	S	C	B	W	H
O	P	F	F	I	F	T	Y	H	V	H	O
R	O	I	C	X	R	Z	J	A	E	I	R
P	W	F	N	U	H	P	L	R	R	R	S
I	E	T	C	A	Y	M	A	I	E	L	E
S	R	K	J	A	H	Q	G	O	D	W	S
R	U	I	S	D	G	S	L	M	N	I	L
C	L	O	A	K	W	R	I	A	E	I	E
E	W	H	I	R	L	W	G	L	F	X	R
I	S	R	A	E	L	F	O	Z	E	T	I
A	W	H	I	R	L	W	I	N	D	K	F

Get Elisha back to the Jordan.

Read this story in 2 Kings 8:1-6

Gehazi pleads with the king

Give everything back to her

2 kings 8:6

Join the dots to find the woman's house.

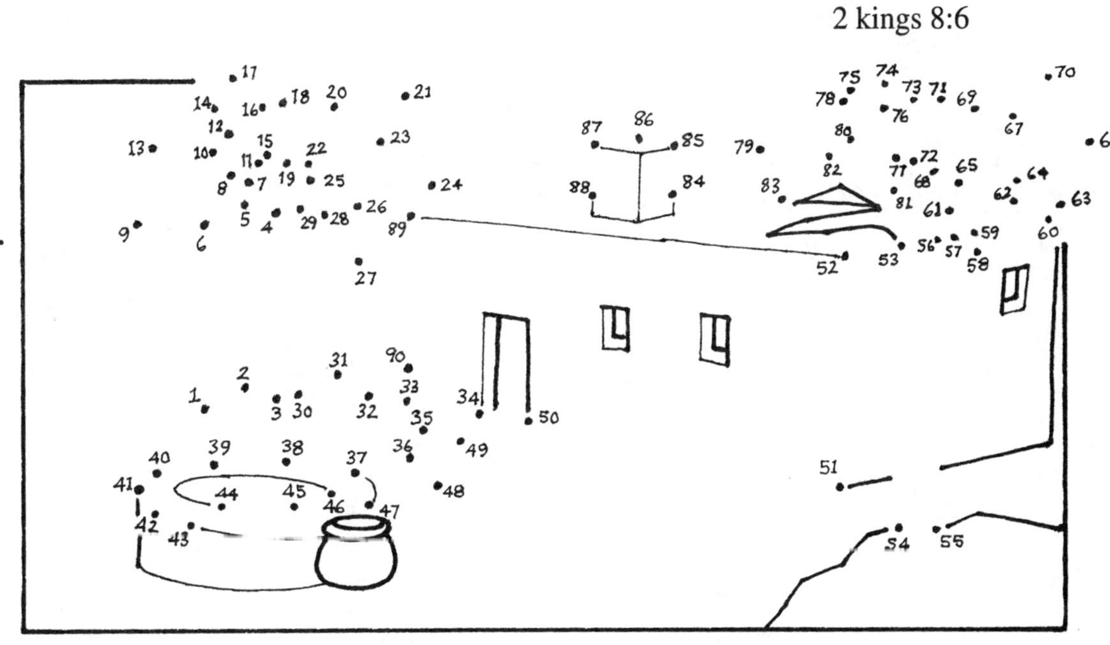

Gahazi isn't doing very well! Help him tell the story, by changing the words in CAPITALS to other words which rhyme with them.

This is the woman whose BUN _ _ _ was
brought back to STRIFE _ _ _ _ by Elisha.
But then there was a HAM IN _ _ _ _ _ _
and she moved away for HEAVEN _ _ _ _ _ TEARS _ _ _ _ _.
Now TREE _ _ _ wants to come MOAN _ _ _ _,
so please give her MOUSE _ _ _ _ _
and SAND _ _ _ _ back to her.

Read this story in Esther 6

Poor Haman thought *he* was going to be honoured!

Pride goes before a disaster

Proverbs 16:18

Finish this picture by joining the dots, and then colour it. Remember to make the clothes very bright.

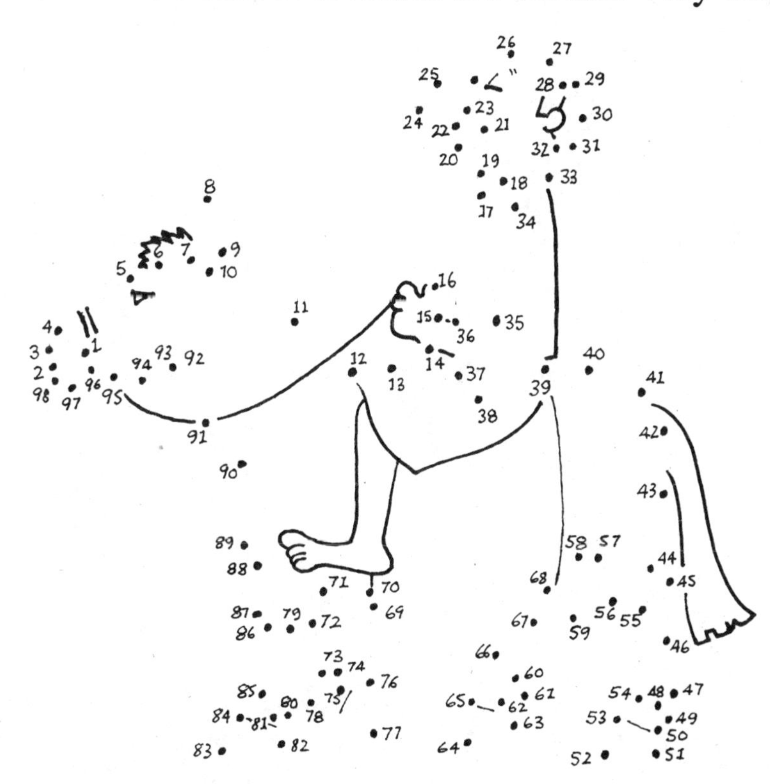

Wordsearch

ANNOUNCE HONOUR
REWARDS MORDECAI
HAMAN POWER
ORNAMENT NOBLEMEN
FRIENDS HORSE WIFE

O	R	N	A	M	E	N	T	F	A	K	T
C	H	J	L	P	E	S	R	O	H	N	O
M	O	R	N	A	M	I	E	W	I	F	U
A	N	F	R	Q	E	S	B	K	M	J	N
P	O	W	E	N	D	W	I	F	E	P	A
H	U	M	D	R	E	W	A	R	X	Z	M
F	R	S	A	E	C	N	U	O	N	N	A
H	O	W	O	U	R	D	R	W	I	F	H
Q	E	F	R	I	E	N	P	E	O	N	U
R	N	E	M	E	L	B	O	N	W	S	I
M	O	R	D	E	C	A	I	G	L	O	V
R	E	W	A	R	B	H	O	R	S	T	P

Read this story in Matthew 4:1-11

Do not put God to the test

Matthew 4:7

Draw a line from each temptation to Jesus's answer.

Turn stones into bread	Jump off the top of the temple	Worship me and do it my way!
Do not tempt God	Worship only God	People need more than just bread

These pictures may look the same, but can you spot ten differences?

Read about this in Matthew 6:5-8

Join up each wordy prayer to the simpler version.
(Draw lines or colour the boxes to match them up)

Which people do you think God is most pleased with?

Messengers from John the Baptist

Read this story in Matthew 11:1-6

Jesus said, "I came to give life - life in all its fulness"
John 10:10

Wordsearch

BAPTIST CHRIST BLIND
DISCIPLES JOHN POOR
PREACHED GOODNEWS
HEARING SEEING LIFE
SUFFER TWELVE TEACH

P	R	E	A	C	H	E	D	A	Q	G	S
T	B	L	I	N	Y	H	C	V	C	O	U
S	U	F	F	E	R	Y	S	N	G	O	F
I	H	N	G	N	I	E	E	S	G	D	F
T	E	A	C	H	Z	D	E	P	A	N	E
P	A	N	H	O	J	L	L	R	H	E	C
A	R	O	D	F	P	J	O	H	X	W	H
B	I	L	N	I	K	O	I	X	P	S	R
A	N	T	C	R	P	B	E	U	B	L	I
P	G	S	U	F	F	F	X	R	T	W	S
T	I	M	E	J	I	E	V	L	E	W	T
D	I	S	C	L	W	D	N	I	L	B	I

Get John's Disciples to Jesus

Read this story in Matthew 19:16-26

You will have riches in heaven

Matthew 19:21

Which of these make you rich on earth, and which in heaven?

These two pictures look the same. Can you find six differences?

A mother's request

Read this story in Matthew 20:20-28

This is not the way among you

Matthew 20:26

What things lead us to Jesus?

Whom can I be helpful to this week?

1 ....

2 ....

3 ....

4 ....

What kind things can I do?

1 ....

2 ....

3 ....

4 ....

Read this story in Mark 3:1-6

How should we treat disabled people? Find the route to happiness.

Jesus heals a blind man

Palm Tree Worksheet 34

Read this story in Mark 8:22-26

He saw everything clearly

Mark 8:25

Replace the words in CAPITALS with rhymes so that the verse makes sense:

Jesus took the FINED _ _ _ _ _ man by the LAND _ _ _ _ and FED _ _ _ him out of the SPILLAGE _ _ _ _ _ _ _ . After HITTING _ _ _ _ _ _ _ _ on the man's THIGHS _ _ _ _ Jesus LACED _ _ _ _ _ _ his BANDS _ _ _ _ _ on him and asked him, 'Can you BE _ _ _ anything? (verse 23)

People or trees? Join the dots to find out

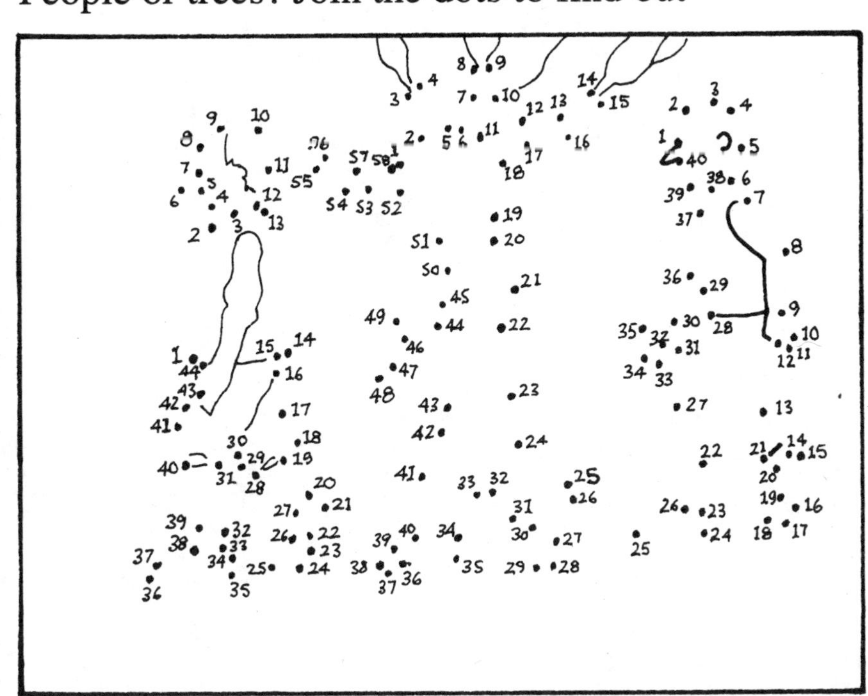

Wordsearch

BETHSAIDA JESUS MAN
BLIND VILLAGE HAND
EYESIGHT CLEARLY
TOUCH INTENTLY

B	E	T	H	S	A	I	X	T	O	U	C
A	B	E	T	H	S	A	I	D	A	M	V
U	Z	Y	L	T	N	E	T	N	I	T	I
N	I	B	I	E	S	V	I	L	L	Y	L
D	N	R	C	N	W	U	D	A	X	L	L
N	T	F	L	B	T	P	S	I	O	R	A
I	E	H	E	K	S	E	Y	E	S	A	G
L	N	D	A	V	M	C	N	G	J	E	E
B	T	G	R	N	C	U	O	T	N	L	J
T	O	U	C	H	D	Q	C	H	X	C	Y
T	H	G	I	S	E	Y	E	L	N	A	M

Read about this in Mark 12:28-34

You are not far from the kingdom

Mark 12:34

Crack the code to find the most important law

1	2	3	4	5	6	7	8	9	0	#
A	D	E	G	H	L	N	O	R	T	V

6	8	#	3		4	8	2		1	7	2

6	8	#	3		8	7	3		1	7	8	0	5	3	9

These two pictures may look the same, but can you spot six differences?

Read this story in Mark 14:43-51

Jesus is with his friends, but some dangerous people are hiding in the garden!

What weapons?

They had
SDROWS _ _ _ _ _ _
and SBLUC _ _ _ _ _

Jesus had
EVOL _ _ _ _
SSENEVIGROF _ _ _ _ _ _ _ _ _ _ _
and GNILAEH _ _ _ _ _ _ _

Who is hiding here? (v.51)
Join the dots to find out.

'Love your enemies and pray for those who hurt you.' Matthew 5:44
MEMORY VERSE.

Can the mob get to Jesus?

Read this story in Luke 4:16-21

The Lord will save his people

Isaiah 61:11

Set the captive free.

Wordsearch

SABBATH
SPIRIT
LORD
SCRIPTURE
SYNAGOGUE
LIBERTY
CAPTIVES
SIGHT
BLIND
FREEDOM
OPPRESSED

A	S	C	R	I	P	T	U	R	N	O	S
F	O	P	R	E	S	S	E	D	B	H	A
R	O	P	P	R	E	S	S	E	D	B	B
E	L	O	R	D	D	J	U	N	P	L	B
E	I	V	T	C	U	G	T	H	G	I	S
D	B	M	A	I	O	S	I	G	H	N	M
O	E	T	L	G	R	L	O	R	R	D	O
X	R	X	A	S	L	I	B	E	R	T	D
I	T	N	F	W	C	A	P	T	I	S	E
C	Y	H	T	A	B	B	A	S	K	R	E
S	C	R	I	P	T	U	R	E	Q	X	R
Y	G	E	S	E	V	I	T	P	A	C	F

Read this Story in Luke 4:38-41

'You are the Son of God!'

Luke 4:41

Draw lines from the correct titles to Jesus.

Join the dots to find Simon's mother-in-law.

Jesus heals

Palm Tree Worksheet 39

Read this story in Luke 8:26-39

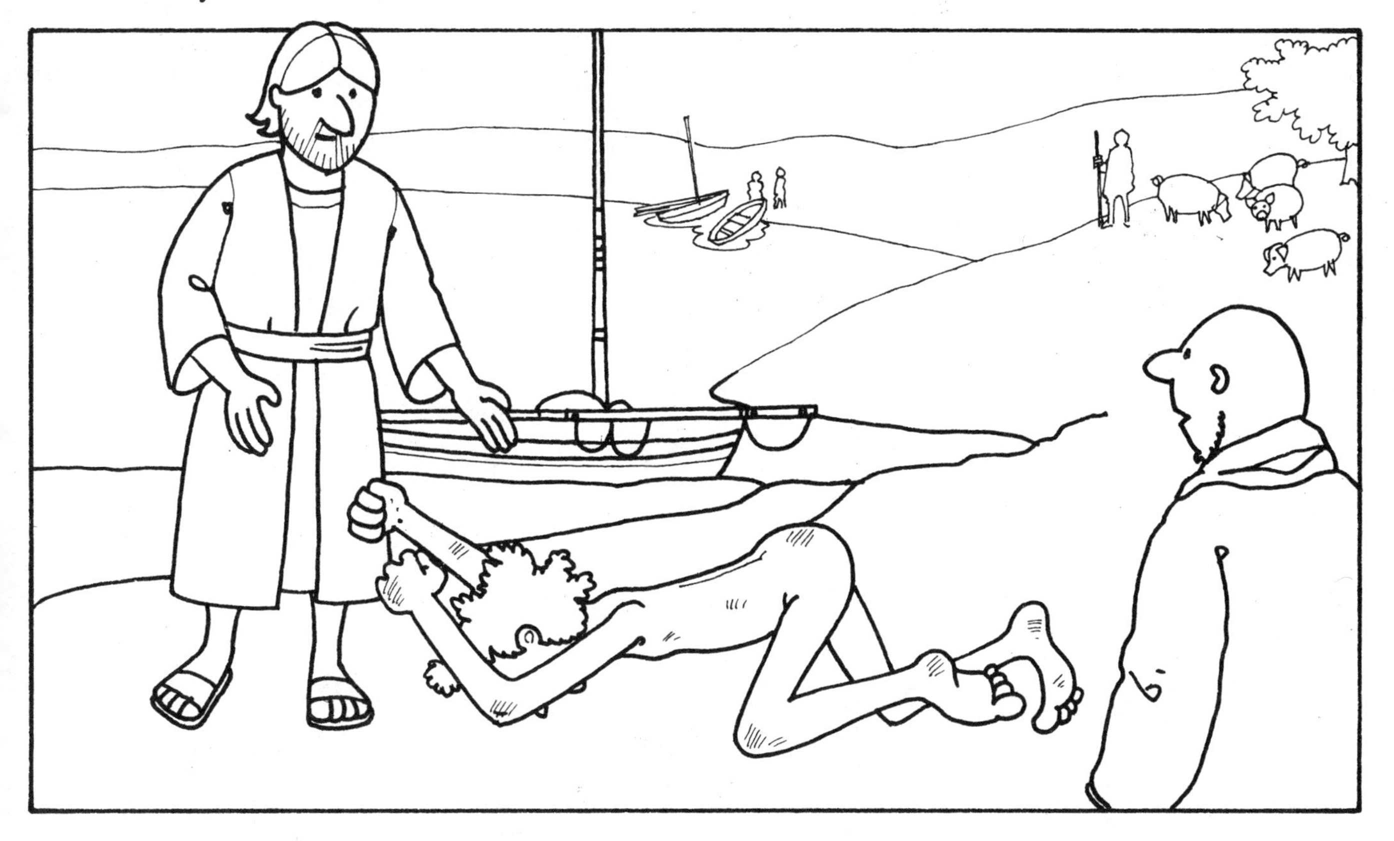

Crack the code to find what Jesus said.

W	T	S	O	N	L	H	G	E	D	A
A	D	E	G	H	L	N	O	S	T	W

O	G		W	H	T		D	S	L	L		A	N	W	D

O	G	T		N	W	E		T	G	H	S

These pictures
nay look
he same
out can
you spot
en differences?

Read this story in John 3:1-21

Born of water and the Spirit

John 3:5

Baptism shows that:

The Spirit produces: (Gal.5:22,23)

EVOL YOJ

ECAEP ECNEITAP LORTNOC-FLES

SSENDNIK YTISORENEG

SSENLUFHTIAF SSENELTNEG

Read this story in John 5:1-18

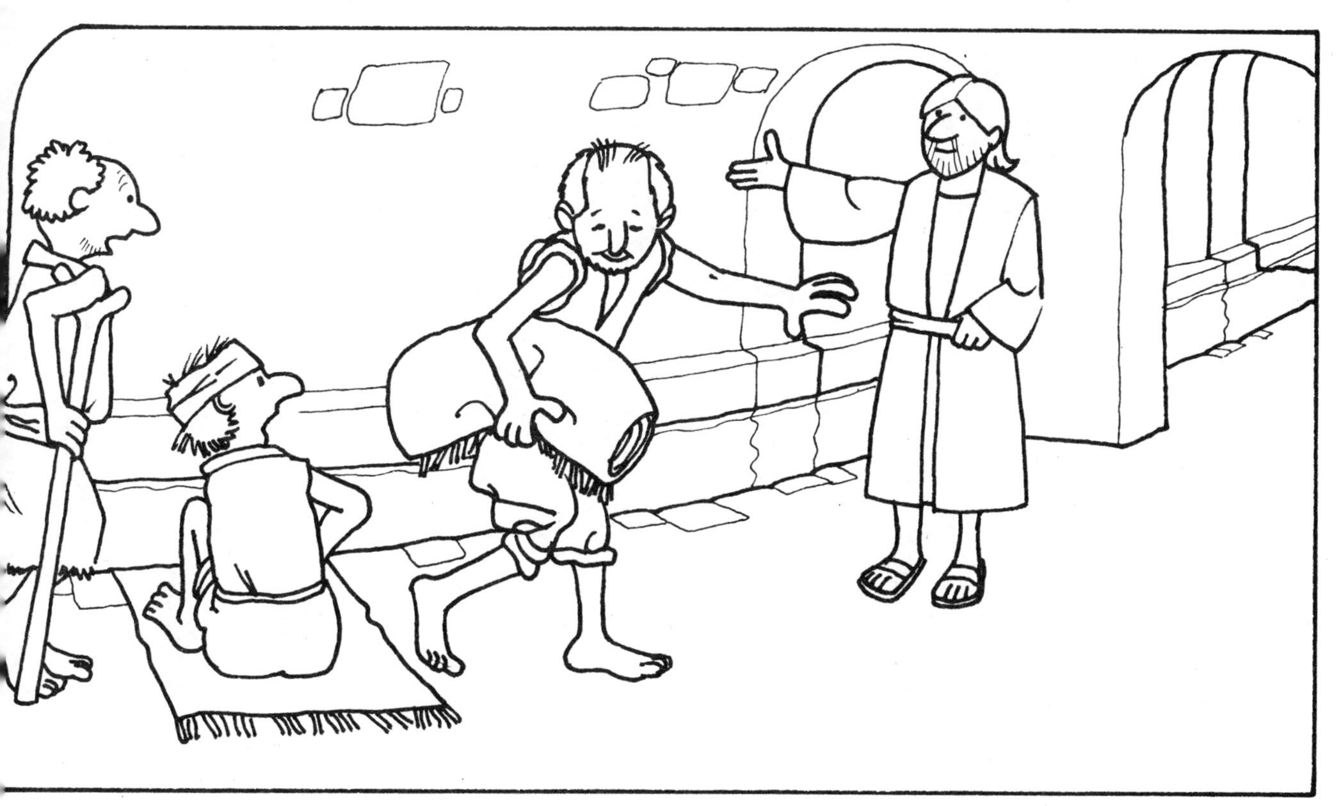

My Father is always working

John 5:17

Here are some of the ways in which God works. Colour them in and think of other things he does.

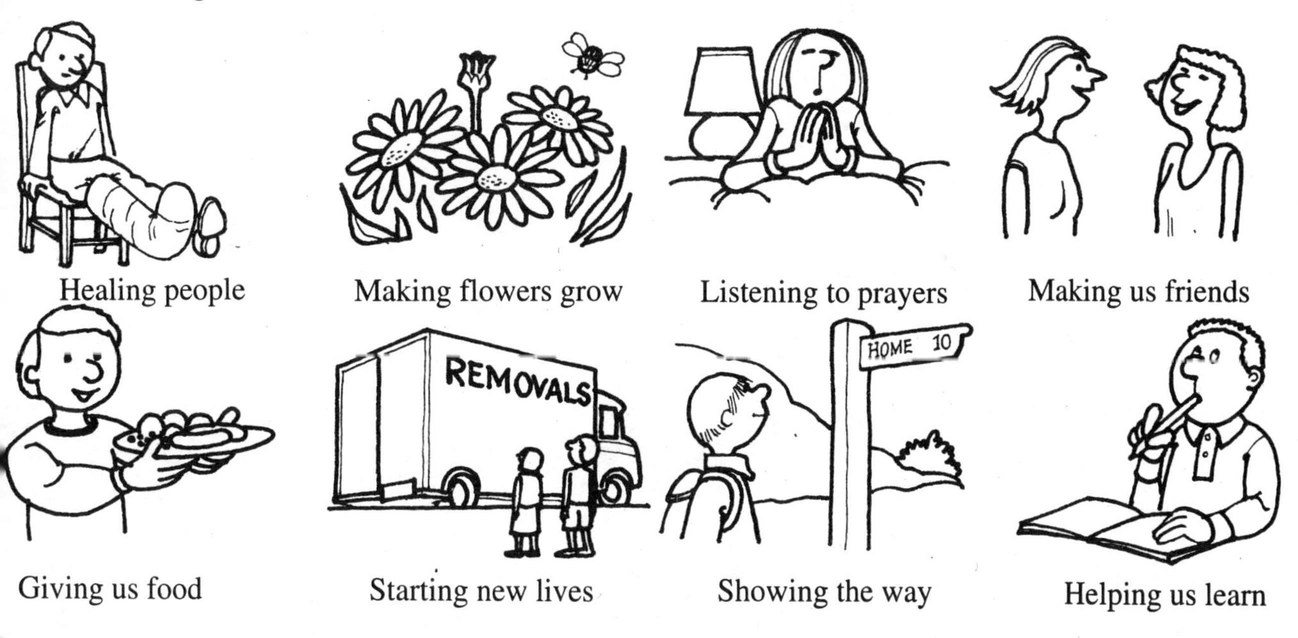

Healing people
Making flowers grow
Listening to prayers
Making us friends
Giving us food
Starting new lives
Showing the way
Helping us learn

True or False?

- ☐ ☐ The man had been ill for ten years.
- ☐ ☐ The pool had five porches.
- ☐ ☐ Jesus had gone to Jerusalem for the festival.
- ☐ ☐ Jesus threw the man into the pool.
- ☐ ☐ The Jewish authorities were pleased with Jesus.
- ☐ ☐ There was a large crowd round the pool.

Read this in John 10:1-5

He calls his own sheep by name

John 10:3

Use rhyming words for the ones in CAPITALS to make the sentence correct.

The man who does not enter the sheepfold by the DATE _ _ _ _ but goes in some other DAY _ _ _ is a LEAF _ _ _ _ _ _ _ and a JOBBER _ _ _ _ _ _ _ . The PAN _ _ _ who goes in through the RATE _ _ _ _ is the shepherd of the HEAP _ _ _ _ _ _ . The LEAP _ _ _ _ _ hear his CHOICE _ _ _ _ _ as he STALLS _ _ _ _ _ his own BLEEP _ _ _ _ _ by FAME _ _ _ _

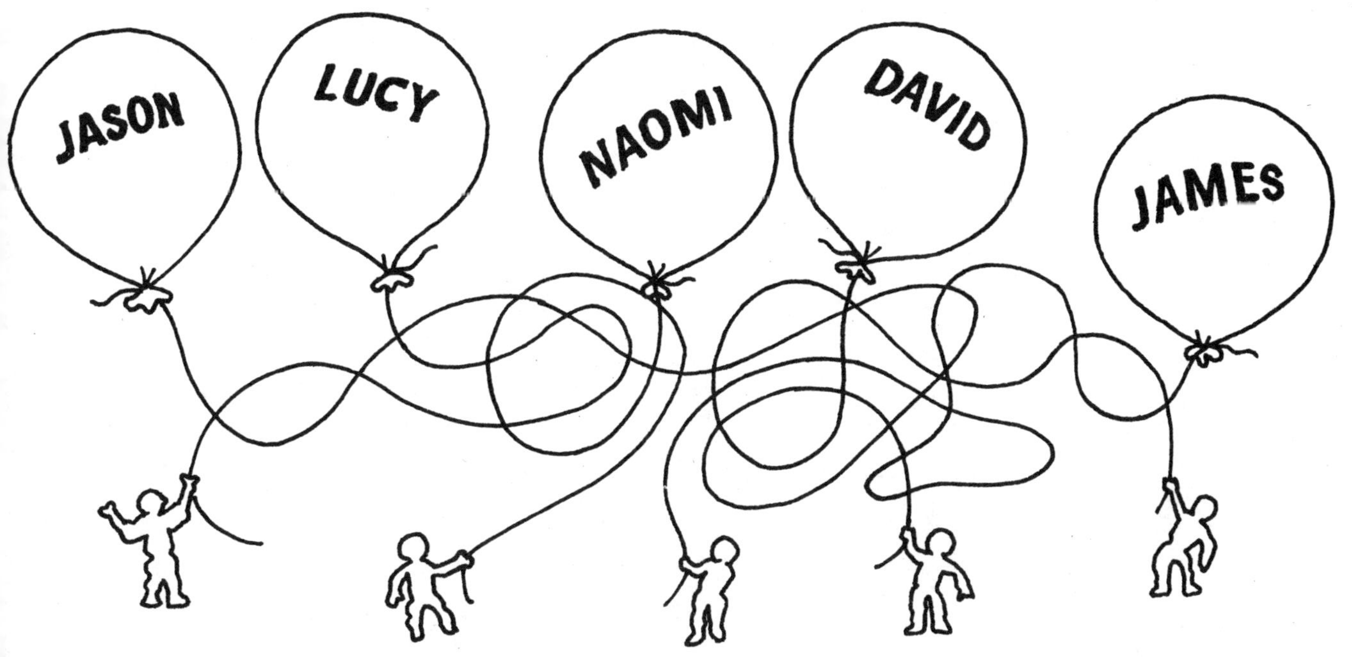

Find the children's names:

Read this story in John 20:11-18

Help Mary get to the disciples with the good news.

These pictures may look the same, but can you spot six differences?

.ead about this in Acts 4:32-37

To each according to need

Acts 4:35

Colour the caring and sharing pictures. Leave the other ones dull!

Jesus wants us to:
(tick for 'yes', cross for 'no')

Criticise each other ☐
Encourage each other ☐
Share ☐
Ignore each other ☐
Grab as much as we can ☐

Read this story in Acts 11:1-18

Do not consider anything unclean that God has declared clean

Acts 11:9

Join up the animals to their names.

Wordsearch

CLEAN UNCLEAN ANIMALS
REPTILES BIRDS PRAYING
VISION SPIRIT BAPTIZED

P	R	A	Y	I	N	T	L	G	A	E	H
D	U	N	C	L	E	A	N	G	Q	K	R
B	A	P	T	I	S	N	N	T	X	B	E
A	N	I	M	A	V	I	S	I	O	N	P
S	E	P	T	L	Y	M	S	P	I	R	T
D	B	V	I	A	J	A	F	B	S	C	I
R	E	P	R	I	L	L	S	P	I	R	L
I	V	P	I	X	R	S	N	D	V	A	E
B	T	I	P	I	C	O	G	A	J	N	S
C	L	E	S	W	G	D	F	U	E	Z	E
A	D	E	Z	I	T	P	A	B	M	L	I
R	E	P	T	I	O	H	C	K	S	F	C

Read this story in Acts 17:16-28

God is not far from any of us

Acts 17:27

Crack the Code to find an important truth.

W	T	S	R	O	N	L	I	H	E	D	C	A
A	C	D	E	H	I	L	N	O	R	S	T	W

A	R		C	H	H		W	E	R

O	N	D		T	O	N	L	S	E	R	I

These pictures may look the same, but can you find six differences?